DDT... etc

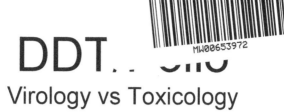

Virology vs Toxicology

Selected First Editions of
Independent Research (1998-2000)
Data Confirmed, Annotated,
with New Material (2014)

by Jim West

Publisher's Cataloging-in-Publication Data

West, Jim, 1947-
DDT/Polio: Virology vs Toxicology / Jim West.
pages cm
Includes bibliographical references.
ISBN: 978-1-941719-04-6 (pbk. b/w)
ISBN: 978-1-941719-00-8 (e-book, color)
1. Toxicology. 2. Virology.
3. Medicine—Research. I. Title.

Contents

Preliminary Notes

This book presents the first editions of Jim West's research into pesticides and polio. These are the original text as published circa 1998-2000, with the addition of up-to-date annotations. Also included is a historical followup, "Positive Results", comparing literature before and after the DDT/Polio publicity of 2000.

New ideas are introduced, new ways to critically explore polio, current as of May 2014. A simple defense is described for the unfairly maligned Rachel Carson. The poliovirus model is critiqued in a most simple manner.

Acknowledgement: Sheri Nakken, John Scudamore, and John Wantling, supporters since first publication; Mitchel Cohen, the calm and fair-minded coordinator of NoSpray Coalition who maintains fair-minded politic to prevail among New York grassroots environmentalists, in their meetings and forums, thereby facilitating West's ability to introduce his research; Jonathan Collin, MD, publisher of *Townsend Letter for Doctors and Patients*, who allowed my DDT/Polio research to be published upon the encouragement of a safely anonymous professor of biology; Anthony Brink, medical critic, author, lawyer and judge, who strongly encouraged.

Legal Disclaimer: The author makes no claim of official authority or expertise. His work is for discussion. It is controversial. It is about science politics. It is not medical advice. Medical advice must be sought from a trusted medical professional.

Annotations are in [brackets]. Emphasis is by <u>underline</u> or **bold**.

Preface, 2014

"Pesticides and Polio" was published in *The Townsend Letter for Doctors and Patients*, June 2000. The article is a distillation of my unpublished book, *DDT/Polio* (1999), over 400 pages. The article and book were the result of independent research, written without the polio arcana of 1959-1954. It represents the first public exposure of the concept since the arcana.

The article was republished soon thereafter by The Weston A. Price Foundation.

The article established simple arguments that could help reveal a ruthless and violent exploitation of the mass market. A decade later, the topic had even reached the mainstream, as Larry King opened his interview with Jenny McCarthy, vaccine critic, with a question about the very existence of poliovirus. McCarthy assured King that she was not so radical.

My graphs were reproduced in the book, *Autism: The Diagnosis, Treatment, & Etiology of the Undeniable Epidemic*, by John Oller, Jr., PhD.

The German biochemist, Stefan Lanka, PhD, wrote, "Recently I found the time to review your polio website. The work is great — and of the greatest importance."

Jon Rappoport, the courageous investigative journalist, has strongly supported my work at his NoMoreFakeNews.com.

My polio graphs have been reconfirmed and reproduced in the book, *Virus Mania*, by Torsten Englebrecht, journalist, and Claus Köhnlein, Doctor of Internal Medicine.

Anthony Brink, leading medical critic, author, lawyer and judge, has strongly supported my work, and led by example.

Vaccine critics referenced the article, while arguing that the underlying rationale for hazardous vaccine programs was untenable germ fear, with Sheri Nakken, RN, an early supporter. The article received praise from naturopaths and chiropractic doctors, such as Tedd Koren, DC and Tim O'Shea, DC.

I've learned that medical critics and environmentalists can be as corrupt as "big corporations", in terms of epistemology. Example:

The Ecologist, the world's most read ecology journal, May 2004, gave me a perverse form of praise. It published a massively error-ridden version of the my DDT/Polio theme, which was listed on its website as a revolutionary "Hot Topic" for six months. After publication, the author, Janine Roberts, stated privately that his article was "built upon" my work, while he was continuing to erase all signs of me from many of my website pages, which he had copied to his website.

My article represents independent research that enabled the discovery of buried, disconnected, unreferenced works, i.e., the arcana of polio toxicology which originated long before Rachel Carson, namely, the works of Biskind, Mobbs, and Scobey. Finding Biskind was finding a lost brother in the time warp. To hear the nearly unspeakable spoken by such a dignified yet humble intelligence was immensely comforting, as I had researched myself far out on a thin limb.

Nowadays it may seem odd to feel that way, yet, in the 1990s, technical skepticism of viruses was not beyond Duesberg. There were arguments in the 1950s among virologists about the nature of viruses. In the 1920s, there were studies that had set the basis for the entire elimination of the term "virus", but these were subverted in scientific literature by the powerful influence of Dr. Thomas Rivers, of the Rockefeller Institute, retired with high military rank, and those dissident studies became another area of arcana, though now revealed through the polio arcana.

The article pushes Biskind to the forefront as much as possible to satisfy the reader's requirement for authority. This must be said, because some authors represent my work falsely, as if my foundation rests on the arcana.

Many dimensions of poliomyelitis are examined in this critique of the two literatures: polio and pesticides. The dimensions are perhaps covered by the terms: polio-culture, philosophy, politics, business, physiology, toxicology, chemistry, biochemistry, epidemiology, and etiology. This approach is broad and every sentence calls for further study.

Mainstream biochemical-medical authority is represented in these articles, and the arguments are within the conventions of mainstream terminology.

For some this work may be mind boggling, too controversial. It is intended to help reestablish commonsense discussions that can restore people's dwindling faith in themselves and their relation to nature. All forms of mainstream media successfully undermine people's natural support systems with 24/7 propaganda, leaving people distanced from themselves, from each other and nature.

The mainstream hierarchy of Modern Medicine strives to weaken lateral, internal, root and natural support systems as if it were jealous of nature. This hierarchial system is behaving normally, striving for its own power against the natural flow of other communication modes. This system is a type of war that is natural in its own sense of being, like the trunk of a tree controlling the growth of branches and leaves. Its requirements are mathematical, not ethical. War is only visible when the leaves of the tree try to reconfigure their fate, which of course, eventually happens as the tree evolves. Individuals benefit from the hierarchial system and suffer from it. As individuals we must maintain our lateral and natural connections.

This work investigates the priestly-political cultures of science, medicine, and health. It is independent and holistic. These might be viewed as disadvantageous, yet, they can also facilitate the essentials, objectivity, honest discovery and interpretation. Since publication, I have been far from independent in the web sense, largely due to the internet and its ability to have like minds globally connected.

Accurate numbers for polio and pesticides are difficult to find. Pesticide distribution data was illegal to disseminate during the 1940s-1970s. The workaround was to use transportation board data.

Text and numbers found scattered throughout mainstream polio literature were collected for this critical work. The gathering of numbers has been a success and it continues as a work in progress. Statistical sources are effectively utilized and portrayed throughout this book. It could be argued that one poignant graph could be substituted for this entire article, and the rest should be up to the U.S. Department of Justice. The mainstream indicts itself with silent avoidance of this topic.

Since 2000, the dilemmae posed by the article have brought many inquiries into the "human condition" (Alexis Carrel's summarization of the severe, tragic and nearly inexplicable political problems). How is it that the unthinkable has become commonplace horror while still remaining unthinkable. Years later, 2014, my continued research has reached some maturation, and should be discussed soon in other works in progress.

By chasing the famous icons of and DDT and polio, this research came into being. DDT shares its causative status with the other persistent pesticides, though DDT had the honor of being mandated by the U.S. government on dairy farms during the upswing of The Great Polio Epidemic.

As published in *Townsend Letter for Doctor's and Patients, June 2000*

A Critique Of Scientific Literature

Pesticides And Polio

by Jim West

Warning

> "It has been alleged that DDT causes or contributes to a wide variety of diseases of humans and animals not previously recognized as associated with any chemical. Such diseases included... poliomyelitis, ...such irresponsible claims could produce great harm and, if taken seriously, even interfere with scientific search for true causes..." (*Handbook of Pesticide Toxicology*, edited by Wayland J. Hayes, Jr. and Edward R. Laws, Academic Press Inc., Harcourt Brace Jovanovich, Publishers, San Diego (1991) 3 volumes, v2p769)

Hayes and Laws were informing their readers about the heretic, Dr. Morton S. Biskind.

In 1953, when Biskind's writings were being published, following the apex of the greatest polio epidemic in the United States, he and the entire public were encountering dramatic images: a predatory poliovirus, nearly a million dead and paralyzed children, iron lungs, struggling doctors, and dedicated nurses. The late president Franklin D. Roosevelt had been memorialized as a polio-victim who was infected with the deadly poliovirus near the beautiful and remote island of Campobello. Positive images were presented regarding scientific progress and the marvels of DDT. Jonas Salk was preparing to move center stage.

Through this intellectually paralyzing atmosphere, Dr. Biskind had the composure to argue what he thought was the most obvious explanation for the polio epidemic: *Central nervous system diseases such as polio are actually the physiological and symptomatic manifestations of the ongoing government and industry sponsored inundation of the world's populace with central nervous system toxins.*

Today, few remember this poignant writer who struggled with the issues of pesticides, issues that Rachel Carson would be allowed to politely bring to public awareness nine years later, as the lead story in *The New Yorker* magazine and then a national best seller, by limiting her focus to the environment and wildlife. Biskind had the audacity to write about human damage. I found "M. S. Biskind" in the endnotes to Hayes and Laws' diatribe. What could possibly have motivated that biased genuflection towards germ theory? Such offerings, commonly written into the final paragraphs of scientific articles, are usually done with an appearance of impartiality.

With great anticipation, I went to a medical library and found Biskind's 10-page article in the *American Journal of Digestive Diseases*, v20 (1953). Presented below are excerpts regarding polio:

> "In 1945, against the advice of investigators who had studied the pharmacology of the compound and found it dangerous for all forms of life, DDT (chloro-pheno-ethane, dichloro-diphenyl-trichloro-ethane) was released in the United States and other countries for general use by the public as an insecticide."

> [...]

> "Since the last war there have been a number of curious changes in the incidence of certain ailments and the development of new syndromes never before observed. *A most significant feature of this situation is that both*

man and all his domestic animals have simultaneously been affected."

"In man, the incidence of poliomyelitis has risen sharply."

[...]

"It was even known by 1945 that DDT is stored in the body fat of mammals and appears in the milk. With this foreknowledge the series of catastrophic events that followed the most intensive campaign of mass poisoning in known human history, should not have surprised the experts. Yet, far from admitting a causal relationship so obvious that in any other field of biology it would be instantly accepted, virtually the entire apparatus of communication, lay and scientific alike, has been devoted to denying, concealing, suppressing, distorting and attempts to convert into its opposite, the overwhelming evidence. Libel, slander and economic boycott have not been overlooked in this campaign."

[...]

"Early in 1949, as a result of studies during the previous year, the author published reports implicating DDT preparations in the syndrome widely attributed to a "virus-X" in man, in "X-disease" in cattle and in often fatal syndromes in dogs and cats. The relationship was promptly denied by government officials, who provided no evidence to contest the author's observations but relied solely on the prestige of government authority and sheer numbers of experts to bolster their position."

[...]

["X-disease"] ...studied by the author following known exposure to DDT and related compounds and over and over again in the same patients, each time following known exposure. We have described the syndrome as follows: ...In acute exacerbations, mild clonic convulsions involving mainly the legs, have been observed. Several young children exposed to DDT developed a limp lasting from 2 or 3 days to a week or more."

[...]

"Simultaneously with the occurrence of this disorder [X-disease] a number of related changes occurred in the incidence of known diseases. The most striking of these is poliomyelitis. In the United States the incidence of polio had been increasing prior to 1945 at a fairly constant rate, but its epidemiologic characteristics remained unchanged. Beginning in 1946 the *rate of increase more than doubled*. Since then remarkable changes in the character of the disease have been noted. Contrary to all past experience, the disease has remained epidemic year after year."

DDT vs Polio (1945-1953)

In the graph below, I provide confirmation of Biskind's observations for 1945-1953, in terms of polio incidence and pesticide production. I have utilized pesticide data from Hayes, et al, which they had obtained from the U.S. Transportation Board. Polio incidence data was gathered from *U.S. Vital Statistics* [and related literature]. Although I argue herein against Hayes' characterization of Biskind's work, credit goes to Hayes for publishing arcane pesticide data. [Graph→]

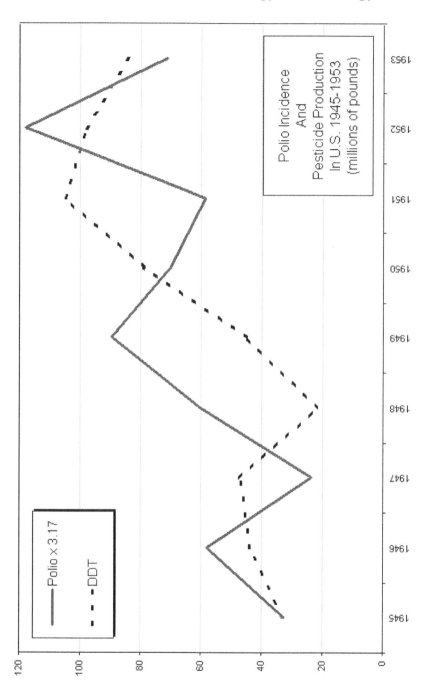

Polio Incidence
And
Pesticide Production
In U.S. 1945-1953
(millions of pounds)

Physiological Evidence

Biskind also describes physiological evidence of DDT poisoning that resembles polio physiology:

> "Particularly relevant to recent aspects of this problem are neglected studies by Lillie and his collaborators of the National institutes of Health, published in 1944 and 1947 respectively, which showed that DDT may produce degeneration of the anterior horn cells of the spinal cord in animals. These changes do not occur regularly in exposed animals any more than they do in human beings, but they do appear often enough to be significant."

He continues, bearing his exasperation in trying to make the obvious plain:

> "When the population is exposed to a chemical agent known to produce in animals lesions in the spinal cord resembling those in human polio, and thereafter the latter disease increases sharply in incidence and maintains its epidemic character year after year, is it unreasonable to suspect an etiologic relationship?"

Before finding Biskind, I had spent months engaged in a nearly futile search for the physiology of acute DDT poisoning. I began to sense that American DDT literature as a whole intends to convey that *DDT is not a dangerous toxin except with regard to its general environmental effects due to persistent bioaccumulation, and that the physiology of acute DDT poisoning is therefore trivial.* DDT literature jumps uniformly from descriptions of symptoms, over physiology, to the biochemistry of DDT-caused dysfunction in nerve tissue.

It was as if detectives had come upon a mass-murder scene and immediately became obsessed with the biochemistry of dying cells around bullet holes, while ignoring the bullet holes.

Eventually, I did find one study of the physiology of acute DDT poisoning by Daniel Dresden (*Physiological Investigations Into The Action Of DDT*, G.W. Van Der Wiel & Co., Arnhem (1949)). This study confirms that DDT poisoning often causes polio-like physiology:

> "Conspicuous histological degeneration was, however, often found in the central nervous system. The most striking ones were found in the cerebellum, mainly in the nucleus dentatus and the cortex cells. Among other things an increase of the neuroglia and a necrotic degeneration and resorption of ganglionic cells was found. The Purkinje cells were less seriously affected than the other neurons. Also in the spinal cord abnormalities of a degenerative nature were found."

> "...such changes were not found invariably... there is neither an obvious relation between the size and spreading of the lesion and the quantity of DDT applied... information of adequate precision about the nature of the anomalies is lacking."

So we find that especially the cerebellum and the spinal cord are histologically affected by DDT.

And more recently, in the works of Scobey, I found that from ancient times to the early 20th century the symptoms and physiology of paralytic poliomyelitis were often described as the results of poisoning. It wasn't until mid-19th century that the word "poliomyelitis" became the designation for the paralytic effects of severe poisoning and polio-like diseases assumed to be germ-caused.

Today, various other forms of the word "polio" are still used in descriptions of the effects of neurotoxins, although usually with regard to paralysis in animals. A search of

Medline ("polio" and "poison") finds numerous contemporary articles where poison causation is attributed to polio. The terminology found: "polio-encephalo-malacia", "polio-myelo-malacia, a neurological picture similar to that of poliomyelitis", "polio-encephalo-myelomalacia", "lumbal polio-myelo-malacia", "cerebro-cortical necrosis (polio-encephalo-malacia)", "multifocal-polio-myelo-malacia", "spinal polio-malacia", "Polio and high-sulfate diets", "Atypical porcine enterovirus encephalo-myelitis: possible interaction between enteroviruses and arsenicals", "Polio-encephalo-malacia and photosensitization associated with Kochia scoparia consumption in range cattle", "bovine polio-encephalo-malacia". [Revised 2011]

In Britain, a farmer turned scientist, Mark Purdey has found substantial evidence that "Mad Cow Disease", a form of polio-like encephalitis, is caused by the government-mandated cattle treatment, a treatment formulated with organophosphate pesticide and a compound similar to thalidomide. Purdey's works can be found on the NIH website (PUBMED ID's 9572563, 8735882, 8735881).

Unlike most scientists, during his research Mark Purdey became legally embroiled with the government, and... "lost his farm, was shot at, blockaded in his home to prevent him giving a lecture, and saw a new farmhouse go up in flames the day he was due to move in." (ENN Daily News — April 8, 1996) [Mark contacted me, saying that much of what is written about him is not accurate. Clarification, however, was precluded by his death, no foul play suspected.]

Morton S. Biskind's writings regarded humans, and fell into disfavor after the successful introduction of the polio vaccines. By October, 1955, Biskind, whose works were often found in established medical journals and who testified before the House of Representatives on the dangers of pesticides, was forced to self-published his writings, one of which I found via an old card catalog. A scan of Medline found no other works by him except for a very tame article in 1972. He died not long thereafter. He was born in 1906.

A Contemporary Study

Below are three graphs that confirm Biskind, utilizing data that spans far beyond his observations. Again, the pesticide data comes from Hayes and Laws.

DDT vs Polio (1940-1970)

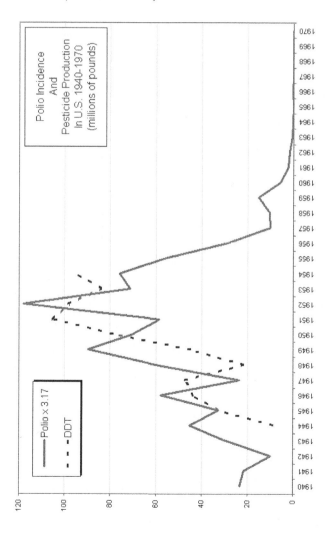

In the following graph I did not include DDT data for the period of 1954 onward because DDT distribution was then being shifted out of the U.S. and into developing nations, while its U.S. production skyrocketed.

BHC vs Polio (1940-1970)
[Graph→]

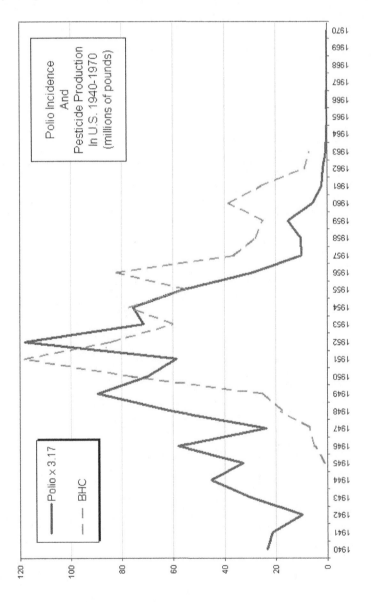

BHC (benzene hexachloride), a persistent, organochlorine pesticide, is several times more lethal than DDT, in terms of LD50 (lethal dosage required to kill 50% of a test population. BHC was produced in 1945-1954 at quantities similar to DDT. In spite of BHC's lethal quality it has received much less publicity than DDT. While DDT was banned for such things as an association with the thinning of eagles' eggs, BHC was phased out of production because it was found, after 15 years, to impart a bad taste to food. It is still used in underdeveloped nations. BHC's correlation with polio incidence is astonishing.

Lead-Arsenic vs. Polio (1940-1970)

After viewing the DDT and BHC graphs above, notice that the period of 1940-46 is unaccounted for in terms of polio-pesticide correlation. The missing piece of the puzzle for this 6-year period is supplied by the lead and arsenic compounds. These CNS toxins have been the major pesticides during the several centuries previous to the advent of the organochlorines in the early 1940s.

   For those who have thought that "organic" food was the norm before the release of DDT to the civilian sector in 1945, the immense production of lead-arsenic compounds seen in this graph is disappointing. This data requires a reconsideration of statements regarding the "natural" quantities of arsenic found in apple seeds, apricots, or almonds, or "natural" chemotherapies derived from seeds where pesticides can accumulate in soil. [Graph→]

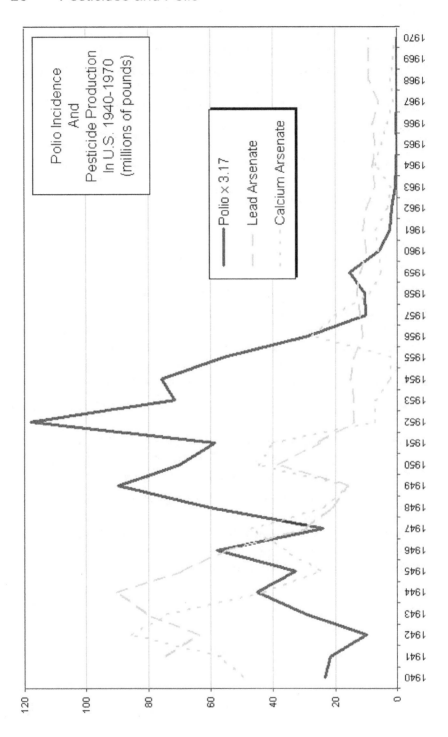

Polio Incidence
And
Pesticide Production
In U.S. 1940-1970
(millions of pounds)

Polio x 3.17
Lead Arsenate
Calcium Arsenate

Pesticides Composite

Virtually all peaks and valleys correlate with a direct one-to-one relationship with each pesticide as it enters and leaves the U.S. market. Generally, pesticide production precedes polio incidence by 1 to 2 years. I assume that this variation is due to variations in reporting methods and the time it takes to move pesticides from factory to warehouse, through distribution channels, onto the food crops, and to the dinner table.

A composite of the three previous graphs, of the persistent pesticides, e.g., lead, arsenic, and the dominant organochlorines (DDT and BHC), are represented. [Graph→]

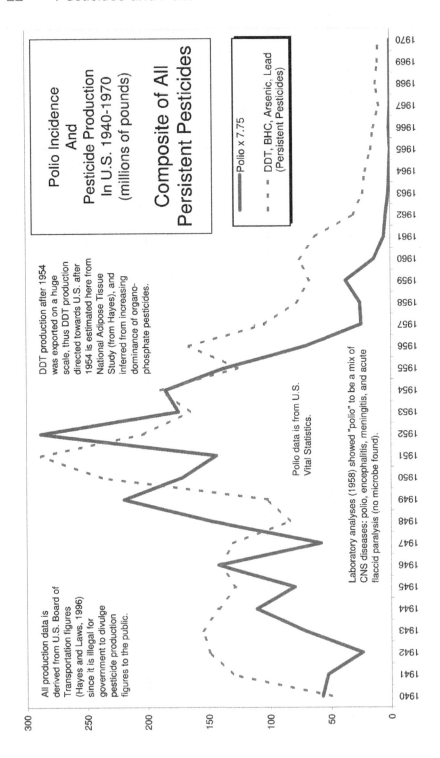

These four chemicals were not selected arbitrarily. These are representative of the major pesticides in use during the last major polio epidemic. They persist in the environment, are neurotoxins that cause polio-like symptoms and polio-like physiology, and were dumped onto/into human food at dosage levels far above that approved by the FDA. They directly correlate with the incidence of various neurological diseases which were called "polio" during the epidemic shown. They were utilized in the "most intensive campaign of mass poisoning in known human history." (quotation from Biskind, op. cit.)

Virus Causation

A clear, direct, one-to-one relation between pesticides and polio over a period of 30 years with pesticides preceding polio incidence in the context of the CNS related physiology just described leaves little room for complicated virus arguments, even as a co-factor, unless there exists more than mere argument or supposition, unless there exists a rigorous proof for virus causality.

Polio shows no movement independent from pesticide movement, as one would expect if a causal virus existed. Popular images, even with doctors, are that a small amount of virus can invade a body (infect) and begin replicating to the point of producing disease, however, in the laboratory, poliovirus does not easily behave in such a predatory manner. Laboratory attempts to demonstrate causality are performed under conditions which are extremely artificial and aberrant.

Virus causality was first established in the mainstream mind by publications of an experiment by Landsteiner and Popper in Germany (1908-1909).

Their method was to inject puree of fecal matter from a diseased human intraperitoneally, through the stomach outer lining. One monkey died and the other became ill. These resulting diseases were not characterized carefully. The study was promoted by journalists claiming virus causation. [Revised 2014.]

The poliovirus presence was assumed (not proven). The weakness of this method is obvious to everyone except certain viropathologists and has recently been criticized by the microbiologist Peter Duesberg regarding a modern-day attempt to establish virus causality for Kuru, another CNS disease (*Inventing The AIDS Virus*, Regnery Press (1996) p16). Since 1908, the basic test for a virus has been repeated successfully many times using monkeys, dogs, and genetically altered mice, and, the injected material has been improved — a saline solution containing purified poliovirus. However, a crucial weakness exists: Humans do not acquire polio via an injection of large quantities of pure poliovirus isolate directly into their brain through a hole drilled in their skull.

If injection into the brain is really a valid test for causality, then this test should serve especially well as a proof for pesticide causality. I propose that pesticides be injected directly into the brains of test animals. If paralysis and nerve degeneration subsequently occur, we would then have proved that pesticides cause polio. It is axiomatic that a theory is only as good as its ability to predict future events. I predict that such a test would prove pesticides to be the most reliable causal factor.

The injection of puree of diseased brain tissue into the brains of dogs was the method preferred by Louis Pasteur to establish virus causality with the CNS disease, rabies. A recent, definitive biography of Pasteur finds him to be a most important publicist for germ theory, a crucial publicist for rabies virus causality, and that his rabies experiments were biased and unsupported by independent studies. (Gerald L. Geison, *The Private Science Of Louis Pasteur*, Princeton University

Press, 1995) Other reasons to doubt claims of virus causality are listed below.

Therefore, in my opinion, even a co-factor theory, where pesticides catalyze predatory poliovirus activity, or where pesticides weaken the immune system to allow opportunistic predatory poliovirus activity, cannot stand up to simple, commonsense explanations that include the concept of a symbiotic virus. Neurotoxins are enough of a cause for neurological disease.

The most obvious theory, pesticide causality, should be the dominant theory. But the opposite exists, a pervasive silence regarding pesticide causality juxtaposed against a steady stream of drama regarding virus causality. In light of the evidence presented herein, the silence could ultimately discredit mainstream medical science, institutions of the environmental movement, and the World Health Organization which just happens to direct both DDT application and polio vaccination world-wide.

Virus Presence

When the symptoms of polio are recognized there is often a claim of virus presence in the body of the polio victim. Sometimes a virus is found. Sometimes that virus is an enterovirus. Sometimes that enterovirus is a poliovirus. During polio epidemics, orthodoxy blames the poliovirus, and therefore, in my argument for the innocence of the poliovirus it is necessary to explain the claims of virus presence and the actual presence of the poliovirus.

Economic Impetus: During the great epidemic of 1942-1962 polio victims were diagnosed with the concept of poliovirus-caused polio, regardless of whether or not the poliovirus was found because the NFIP (March of Dimes) funds paid only for this kind of polio. Therefore, if patients were going to spend time hospitalized, in iron lungs, undergoing therapy, it would have been imperative, economically, for the hospital to diagnose them in this way (Julie Silver, "Three Signs of Post/Polio Problems", *Accent on Living*, Winter (1995), v40). Thus, presence of poliovirus in poliomyelitis was not always determined in order to diagnose polio.

Other Viruses: Even if one believes in virus culpability, other viruses are also claimed by orthodoxy to be the cause of polio-like CNS diseases which are "clinically indistinguishable" from polio. A positive finding for the poliovirus has not always been necessary to diagnose polio. In 1958, laboratory analyses of diagnosed polio victims found poliovirus in only 56% of the cases. A mix of 10 or more pathogens can often be associated with a single diagnosed case of polio.

> "Coxsackievirus and echoviruses can cause paralytic syndromes that are clinically indistinguishable from paralytic poliomyelitis."
> (John H. Menkes, *Textbook Of Child Neurology*, 5th ed., page 420)

Benign Virus: The poliovirus is considered to have been endemic throughout the world going back to ancient times yet this is not the case with paralytic polio according to Arno Karlen (*Man and Microbes*, G.P. Putnum's Sons (1995)) who writes that "polio virus lives only in people; it probably adapted to the human small intestine countless millennia ago." He continues with, "some historians have claimed that [paralytic] polio goes back to ancient Egypt; it may, but the evidence is thin."

Karlen makes sense here in view of the pesticide graphs and Biskind's arguments, however, Karlen goes on to write that "the first undisputed case dates from the late eighteenth century." This statement, however, must be invalid (in its attempt to establish polio images that have a basis in early history) because of Menkes' statement that other viruses can also be causal for polio symptoms and because common poisons such as arsenic and lead compounds can cause polio-like symptoms. Thus, Karlen's offer of an undisputed case as early as the late 18th century can be no more than a guess.

Orthodox medical literature, in its own terms, can offer no evidence that the poliovirus was anything else than benign until the first polio epidemic (Sweden, 1887). This small epidemic occurred 13 years after the invention of DDT (Germany, 1874), 14 years after the invention of the first mechanical pesticide crop sprayer (1873), which was used to spray formulations of water, kerosene, soap, and arsenic. The epidemic also occurred immediately following an unprecedented flurry of pesticide innovations. This is not to say that DDT was causal for the first polio epidemic, as arsenic was then in widespread use and DDT is said to have been merely an academic exercise. However, DDT, or any of several neurotoxic organochlorines already discovered, could have caused the first polio epidemic if it had been used experimentally as a pesticide. DDT's absence from early literature is little assurance that it was not used.

Poliovirus is an enterovirus. There are at least 72 known enteroviruses discovered to date. According to Duesberg, many enteroviruses are harmless "passenger viruses". In view of the herein revised polio images, probably unknown to Duesberg, it is reasonable that we also view poliovirus as harmless, outside of extreme laboratory conditions.

The Symbiotic Poliovirus

Having now established the possibility of an innocent poliovirus, its presence in polio can be explained as follows:

Accelerated Genetic Recombination: Genetic recombination is accelerated whenever a biological system is threatened (*Molecular Approaches to Environmental Biology* (1996) The proliferation of viruses can often be part of this process.

The presence of pesticides is threatening to a biological system.

The SOS Response: When a cell is critically threatened, accelerated genetic recombination (which may include virus proliferation) is just one of a set of events that may occur. This set of events is called the "SOS Response" which is known to be triggered by exposure to toxins or radiation (Mark Ptashne, *A Genetic Switch* (1992) p62).

Arnold Levine (*Field's Virology*, p6) provides an example:

> "When lysogenic bacteria were lysed [split open] from without, no virus was detected. But from time to time a bacterium spontaneously lysed and produced many viruses. The influence of ultraviolet light in inducing the release of these viruses was a key observation that began to outline this curious relation between a virus and its host."

Is it only ironic that common medical procedures such as chemotherapy, radiation therapy, and the use of toxic pharmaceuticals, accelerate genetic recombination and thus the potential for a necessary virus proliferation?

The Ames Assay Test: The SOS Response is utilized in the Ames Assay Test, a standard test whereby chemical toxicity is determined. According to procedure, bacteria are exposed to a chemical solution in question, and if, thereby, it is found that genetic recombination accelerates via the spontaneous proliferation of viruses from these bacteria then the chemical is determined to be a toxin. The phenomena is sensical, the bacteria being analogous to a poker player with a bad hand who must request an exchange of cards and a re-shuffled deck to improve the possibilities for survival. In the Ames Assay Test, bacteria are concerned with their genetic "hand" in order to improve their abilities to metabolize toxins, create utilizations for toxins, and shield against toxins. Thus they engage in this well-known phenomena, "gene shuffling", facilitated by virus proliferation.

Thus, I propose that the poliovirus is a symbiotic virus (and possibly a dormant virus) that behaves in a manner suggested by the phenomena found in the Ames Assay Test, a test used to determine toxicity.

One could object to the Ames Test analogy on the grounds that because the Ames Test utilizes prokaryote cells (bacteria-like cells) rather than eukaryote cells (nucleus-containing cells that comprise multicellular tissue) and because it is asserted that poliovirus invokes damage by infecting eukaryote cells, the explanation is invalid.

However, the evolution of eukaryotes includes an inheritance of structures and functions inherited from symbiotic unions of prokaryotes. Eukaryotes continue to possess to this day prokaryote functionality such as found in the genetic independence of the organelles within the eukaryote cells, such as mitochondria (Lynn Margulis and Dorion Sagan, *What Is Life?* (1995), and, Lynn Margulis, Dorion Sagan, *Slanted Truths: Essays on Gaia, Symbiosis, and Evolution* (1997)). Thus, generalizations derived from the Ames Test can contribute to a valid hypothesis for the presence of poliovirus in "polio".

Dormant Virus: Thus, when a cell is critically threatened by toxins (or radiation) it can invoke survival mechanisms (the SOS Response) such as the suspension of metabolism, or the activation of <u>dormant</u> viruses, triggering their proliferation from the cell. The words "dormant" and "latent" are used conventionally to describe such viruses, but these words are not my preference because they imply that viruses are only externally generated and are found in the cell in a condition of temporary rest (dormancy). In cyclical phenomena, such as the life cycle of the virus, the "starting point" is a political-philosophical decision. The orthodox virus image (possibly a projection of the orthodox mind) is of an external, selfish, non-living parasite that tricks cells into infecting themselves with the virus and then to replicate said virus with cell machinery. Dormant viruses are publicized as external life forms that spend most of their time (as much as several decades) waiting inside cells, awaiting activation to perform parasitic activities. However, orthodoxy itself states that virus evolution originates from the genetic material of cells, and extremely recently in genetic history (see item 7, below).

Gene Sharing: Viruses represent shared capability, shared data, and data in transit. They are genetic couriers. Shared data decreases the burden on each cell to carry all capabilities. Capability, in the form of genetic information, can be stored in the environment as virus "gene packets", and different capabilities can be stored in different cells, just as humans each have, to some degree, uncommon capabilities which are shared with the community as needed. In the microbiotic world, when a particular capability is needed, cells share genetic information from the dynamically changing universal library of free floating genetic material, such as exists in viruses, free organelles, symbiotic parasites, and free nucleic acid, in addition to straight sexual intercourse where nucleic acid is transferred directly from cell to cell. It could be said that cells can carry unused (dormant) genetic information in the form of nucleic acid and when that information is required, share it by activating virus proliferation.

For example, in terms of disease, a symbiotic virus presence could be explained as a provider of capabilities to facilitate particular cathartic mechanisms which are appropriate for particular toxic or stressed environments. These cathartic mechanisms are manifested as disease symptoms, in the form of masses of sacrificed leucocytes, obviously found in boils, pimples, and pocks. Orthodoxy gives the label "transduction" to the processes of virus infection. Transduction is one of the several possible modes of inter-cellular transport of genetic material. Cells can use transduction to move genetic data from cell to cell without going through the process of formalized "male-female" sexual processes. This data is routinely used to alter their structure and metabolism processes dynamically, without engaging in the slower, more formal reproduction cycles.

The concept of the symbiotic virus is explained in *Encyclopedia Britannica, Macropaedia* (1990) p507:

> "Although viruses were originally discovered and characterized because of the diseases they cause, most viruses that infect bacteria, plants, and animals (including humans) do not cause disease. In fact, bacteriophages [bacteria viruses] may be helpful in that they rapidly transfer genetic information from one bacterium to another, and viruses of plants and animals may convey genetic information among similar species, aiding the survival of their hosts in hostile environments."

Britannica continues with a thanks to industrial biotechnology, that humans too may some day enjoy such capabilities:

> "This could in the future be true for humans as well. Recombinant DNA biotechnology may allow genetic defects to be repaired by injecting afflicted persons with harmless viruses that carry and integrate functional genes to supplant defective ones."

And it is admitted in mundane language that, as part of nature, humans may already possess these functions:

> "Such events may actually occur in nature in the transmission of "good" viruses from one person to another."

Thus, the greatest threat to biotech profit is a symbiotic view of mosquitoes and viruses. Could this account for certain aspects of the current "war" against virus-carrying mosquitoes?

Virus Contradictions

The concept of a predatory poliovirus becomes less certain in the context of these uncommonly known virus facts:

1) Poliovirus "[I]nfectosomes have yet to be experimentally demonstrated..." (Roland R. Rueckert, under the subtitle, "Infection: A Rare Event" in *Field's Virology*.)

2) "Eukaryote cells have a wide arsenal of activities to control the half-lives of mRNAs, and these nucleases have made it difficult to isolate intact RNA viral genomes from cells." ("Virus Evolution", Ellen G. Strauss, et al, *Fields Virology*, Lippincott - Raven Publishers, Philadelphia (1996), v1p163)

In view of item 1, this appears to be another careful way of saying "never".

3) The poliovirus does not always infect in accordance to its notoriety, "For every 200 or so virus particles that encounter a cell, only one will successfully enter and replicate, so research in this area is often confounded by the rarity of successful entry." (http://cumicro2.cpmc.columbia.edu/PICO/Chapters/Cellular.html defunct URL)

4) Only herpes virus has been traced enroute to site of disease from site of infection. "Viruses during retrograde transport on their way up to the cell bodies have so far been localized ultrastructurally only in the case of herpes simplex and herpes virus suis." (Martin E. Schwab and Hans Thoenen, *Encyclopedia of Neuroscience*, edited by George Adelman, pub, Birkhaüser Bros. Inc., Boston (1987) Chapter 39, p102-3)

5) The poliovirus has been electro-photographed in cell tissue. Due the lack of any photos of poliovirus as an

infectosome, these photos should be interpreted as evidence of the cell's SOS response rather than of polio causality. Electro-micro-photography ("EM") has existed for several decades and poliovirus is the most studied virus, and yet there is no photograph of an infectosome. An infectosome is a "membrane-associated particle... which transfers genomic viral RNA through the membrane." (*Field's Virology* (1996) p635)

6) "It seems likely that all viruses trace their origins to cellular genes and can be considered as pieces of rogue nucleic acids." (*Encyclopedia Britannica, Micropaedia* (1997) "Virus")

7) The point in history when known viruses began their evolution has been calculated by molecular biochemists who have interpolated backwards through time the speed and direction of virus evolution. They found that "most viruses we know today have probably evolved since the last ice age."("Virus Evolution", Ellen G. Strauss, et al, *Field's Virology* (1996) v1 p164)

8) Viruses are involved in a process called transduction, one of the three modes of genetic transfer between cells, a process that can accelerate genetic recombination when cells are critically threatened by toxins.

9) Virus infection is used by clone technology to transfer genetic material into cells.

10) "Genetic information moves between viruses and their hosts to the point where definitions and classifications begin to blur." (*Field's Virology* (1996) p6)

11) In terms of genetic similarity, "[T]here was a remarkable continuum..." from virus to host. (*Field's Virology* (1996) p6)

12) "Carrel (1925) was able to produce tumors resembling Rous' sarcoma and transmissible by cell-free filtrates with indol, arsenic, or tar in chicken embryo. Carrel's

observations have been confirmed by other workers. Fischer (1926), by treating cultures of normal cells with arsenic obtained on one occasion a filtrable virus capable of causing tumors." (Ralph R. Scobey, M.D., "Poliomyelitis Caused by Exogenous Virus?", *Science*, v71 (1954))

Any of the items listed above can be used to direct work towards a refreshing view of viropathology. For instance, Alexis Carrel and Albert Fischer's experiments, in 1925-1926, preceded the discovery of the cellular SOS Response by decades. Their work is important in its impact on the basic tenants of viropathology, the contemporary proofs of virus causality, and definitions of immunity. Carrel, who happens to be one of the most recognized of all the Nobel Laureates, has stated without equivocation that the Rous sarcoma tumour is not infective, is caused by an agent within the cells themselves, yet is transmissible by cell-free Berkfeld filtrate of tumour extract. He states that the agent could not be a virus because of his assumption that a virus is an external, disease causing, infectious entity. In retrospect such statements reveal the first (unrecognized) discovery of the dormant retrovirus, and toxic causality for cancer. These landmark experiments are very simple, very clear, and totally ignored by orthodoxy.

If one views Carrel and Fischer as a reinforcement of the symbiotic virus paradigm, then strong alternative views can be presented:

In the case of classical induction of disease by injection of extremely high quantities of virus, the alternative view would be that the presence of such quantities of virus serve as an informational context, a context that indicates imminent toxic death to naïve tissue, with an expected tissue reaction (disease). Or in other words, disease induction (via injection) is no more than an over-reaction (like jumping out of a window when someone yells "fire") in terms of inflammation and catharsis (disease manifestations).

Thus, a) the inducement of disease by the injection of high-quantities of virus, and b) the acquired immunity in survivors of these injections, can both be viewed as parlor tricks, utilized to demonstrate virus causality for disease.

Conclusion

The word "virus" is ancient Latin, meaning "slime" or "poison". Mainstream science admits that most viruses are harmless, yet the word "virus" adds to a biased and highly promoted language of fear regarding nature. Definitions of viruses range from "pathogenic" to "not usually pathogenic" the more popular the media source, the more frightening the definition. Less fearful definitions would change the relationship between the medical industry and its "patients".

Paradoxically, early virus studies considered virus filtrates to be a poison, not a microbe, thus the name virus. Today, we know that viruses are information.

Now, nearly a half-century later, the validity of Dr. Biskind's work appears even more certain. Again, according to Biskind:

> "It was even known by 1945 that DDT is stored in the body fat of mammals and appears in the milk. With this foreknowledge the series of catastrophic events that followed the most intensive campaign of mass poisoning in known human history, should not have surprised the experts. Yet, far from admitting a causal relationship so obvious that in any other field of biology it would be instantly accepted, virtually the entire apparatus of communication, lay and scientific alike, has been devoted to denying, concealing, suppressing, distorting and attempts to convert into its opposite, the overwhelming evidence. Libel, slander and economic boycott have not been overlooked in this campaign."

The unique correlations between CNS disease and CNS toxins present a variety of research opportunities not only in medical science, but political science, philosophy, media studies, psychology, and sociology.

Bibliography

Aristotle, *The Politics*, Penguin Classics, Penguin Books (1962, reprinted 1992)

Morton S. Biskind, M.D., "Public Health Aspects of the New Insecticides", *American Journal of Digestive Diseases*, New York (1953) v20 p331

Casarett and Doull's Toxicology, The *Basic Science of Poisons, 5th ed.*, pub. McGraw-Hill (1996)

Daniel Dresden, *Physiological Investigations Into The Action Of DDT*, G.W. Van Der Wiel & Co., Arnhem (1949)

Peter Duesberg and Brian J. Ellison, *Inventing the AIDS Virus*, Regnery Pub., 1996.

Thomas R. Dunlap, DDT: *Scientists, Citizens, and Public Policy*, Princeton University Press (1981)

"The Federal Insecticide, Fungicide, and Rodenticide Act", *Federal Statutes* (1947) Volume 61, p163

Fields Virology, edited by B. N. Fields, et al, Lippincott - Raven Publishers, Philadelphia (1996)

Gerald L. Geison, *The Private Science Of Louis Pasteur*, Princeton University Press, 1995.

Wayland J. Hayes, Jr., Edward R. Laws, Jr., *Handbook of Pesticide Toxicology* (3 volumes), Academic Press, Inc., Harcourt Brace Jovanovich, Publishers, San Diego (1991)

Richard T. Johnson, at the Department of Neurology, Johns Hopkins University School of Medicine, published in *Annals of the New York Academy of Sciences*, 1995 and excerpted in Jane Colby, *ME: The New Plague*, First and Best in Education, Ltd, 1996.

Arno Karlen, *Man and Microbes*, G.P. Putnum's Sons, 1995.

The Landsteiner and Popper study, first published in Germany, was reported in Robert W Lovett, MD. The Occurrence of Infantile Paralysis in Massachusetts in 1908. *Boston Medical and Surgical Journal*, July 22, 1909.

Lynn Margulis, Dorion Sagan, *Slanted Truths: Essays on Gaia, Symbiosis, and Evolution*, Copernicus, New York (1997)

Robert S. Mendelsohn, M.D., *Confessions of a Medical Heretic*, Contemporary Books, Chicago (1979)

John H. Menkes, *Textbook Of Child Neurology, 5th ed.*, Williams & Wilkins (1995), p420.

"Polio Packet", Centers for Disease Control, 1959.

"Public Law 518", *Federal Statutes* (1954) Volume 68, p511

"Public Law 905", *Federal Statutes* (1956).

Mark Ptashne, *A Genetic Switch*, Cell Press and Blackwell Scientific Publications, 50 Church St., Cambridge, MA 02138 (1992)

Mark Purdey, at NIH website (PUBMED ID's 9572563, 8735882, 8735881) and in *Wise Traditions*, Spring 2000 and Spring 2002.

The National Adipose Tissue Survey, reported in *Handbook of Pesticide Toxicology*, edited by Wayland J. Hayes, Jr. and Edward R. Laws, Academic Press Inc., Harcourt Brace Jovanovich, Publishers, San Diego, 1991, p 303.

Robert Richter and Ruth Norris, Pills, *Pesticides And Profits*, North River Press, Inc. (1982)

Ralph R. Scobey, MD. The Poison Cause of Poliomyelitis and Obstructions to Its Investigation. *Archive of Pediatrics*, April 1952.

Julie Silver. Three Signs of Post-Polio Problems. *Accent on Living*, Winter 1995, v 40.

U.S. Vital Statistics, U.S. Government Printing Office, Washington, D.C.

Jack Trombadore, "An Introduction to Post Polio Syndrome", *New Jersey Polio Network Newsletter*, Fall (1995)

Franklin D. Roosevelt At Campobello

by Jim West (1998)

[The unprecedented toxicological investigation of FDR/Polio.]

Mainstream Images

Franklin D. Roosevelt is struck by the poliovirus at his summer resort on the remote, edenesque island of Campobello.

The author, June Goodfield, portrays these conventional images in "Courage in adversity", *World Health* (Jan-Feb, 1995). This mentions the Bay:

> "FDR, aged 39, arrived at Campobello in 1921 exhausted, but on 10 August, after an active day, he decided he wanted to swim. So he jogged two miles to swim in the icy waters of the Bay of Fundy. Early that evening he felt chilled and went to bed. The next day he had a high fever, and pain in his back and legs. By Friday he couldn't move his legs at all."

This mentions a pond:

> [Johnson family describes a modern day visit to Campobello.] "It was at Campobello that F.D.R. contracted polio. Among many other activities, he swam at Glensevern Pond the day he became ill. Upon our return to the camp, Charles and the girls went for a cold dip (or wade) at this pond, which is near the campsite.

The water was red, they told Maman when they returned." (Johnson family tourists [source now defunct])

This mentions the Bay and a lake [and a fire]:

"During one day in August of 1921 that echoes the manic energy of his cousin Teddy Roosevelt, Franklin had sailed with visitors and fallen into the bay, remembering later that he had "never felt anything so cold as that water." He tried to shake off a sudden malaise by leading his children on a two-mile jog through the woods to swim in a lake, and then they all helped put out a fire on a deserted island. That night he collapsed into a painful, paralytic illness that was only diagnosed as polio at the end of several awful weeks. After that, FDR revisited his beloved island only three times." (American Heritage, Vol 52, Number 5)

The descriptions are fairly typical, limited to portrayals of a wealthy, connected, intelligent, healthy man who has allowed himself to become over-exhausted and exposed to cold, intimating that his immune system was weakened, and that he thus was overcome by parasitic microbes, i.e., the predatory poliovirus while swimming in a remote, natural environment. The stories are told as a mother would describe her child catching a "cold".

Another source focuses on other aspects without contradictions:

"In August 1921, FDR was summering in Campobello, New Brunswick, Canada. After returning from Washington and New York, he took his family sailing on 10 August and on the way home spotted on a nearby island a forest fire, which he and his son fought. When he returned to his cottage, he felt a chill and went to bed. The next morning he found that his left leg dragged and was too weak to sustain his weight. By night-fall his temperature had risen to 102 degrees, and he had considerable pain in his legs and back. FDR had not become exposed to polio at Campobello, since the incubation period for the virus ranges from three to thirty-five days."

"He may have contracted the disease during the summer in Washington or at a Boy Scout outing in New York. After initial misdiagnosis by the local family doctor, FDR's uncle Fred Delano consulted Dr. Samuel Levine at the Harvard Infantile Paralysis Commission, who in turn diagnosed the illness as poliomyelitis. They reached Dr. Robert Lovett, the foremost specialist on infantile paralysis (as polio was then called), and shortly Lovett was on his way to Campobello."
(Franklin D. Roosevelt, His Life And Times: An Encyclopedic View, Edited by Otis L. Graham, Jr. and Meghan R. Wander., (c) G. K. Hall & Co. (1985), p332)

The combined effect of the two images is that FDR was infected by the poliovirus and that through overexertion and exposure to cold he was stricken with paralytic polio.

Missing Images

There should have been a consideration of the obvious toxicology.

The environmental context of a case of acute paralysis should not be limited to "icy waters". "Polluted waters" should be included because of the existence of heavy industry directly upstream from Roosevelt's swim site. (*Encyclopedia Britannica Micropaedia* (1986))

"St. John's, St. Andrew's, Digby and Hantsport during the late 19th and early 20th century were the sites of varied industries, shipbuilding, oil refining, brewing, tanning, clothing manufacturing of hardware, engines, paint, furniture, lumbering, shipping, shipbuilding, and several deep water harbours."

The image of an island in a natural setting is now deflated. The causal image of "swimming in icy water" is now deflated. The "red" water in the pond might indicate iron, that the pond was a catch basin for some industry. [The fire should have been described as an exhaust source of formaldehyde, carbon monoxide, and NOx, all extremely poisonous and capable of causing symptoms of polio.]

The unpleasant reality of industrial pollution enters the scene.

All of the industries, listed above, utilized and, according to common practice at the time, dumped chlorinated hydrocarbons into the waterways leading into the Bay of Fundy. St. John Harbor was a deep-water harbor suitable for international shipping. Ships dumped chemicals from storage and bilges prior to loading or inspections. In later years, a major hydroelectric project would be planned for this industrial bay region. In 1921 toxic chemical dumping regulations were severely lacking.

A study in 1964 by chemist Soren Jensen found evidence of unpublicized global pollution of DDT-like chemicals (PCBs) during the early part of the 20th century.

In 1971, scientists chose the Bay of Fundy as the site for a study of high levels of DDT and DDT-like chemicals in porpoises. (Gaskin, Holdrinet & Frank (1971), from *Handbook of Ecotoxicology*, pub. Blackwell Science Ltd., London (1994, 1998), p384).

The Bay of Fundy, like most bays can be viewed as a huge lake that opens towards the ocean. It contains water from rivers and the ocean's oscillating tidal flow. The Bay has an immense volume as can be known from its width which ranges 30 to 50 miles, and this volume reduces the effective flow to less than a crawl. Thus, the organochlorines and other dangerous wastes flow slowly in various concentrations, surrounding Campobello, as they drift from several industrial sites, certainly St. Andrews, probably St.

John, and possibly Digby, towards the Atlantic. [Google Map's red balloon is FDR's location.] [Map→]

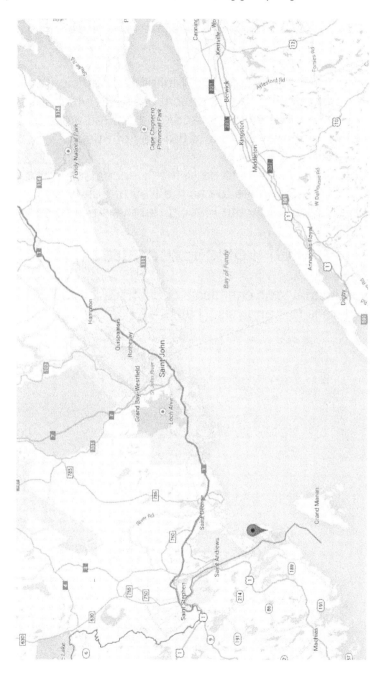

Paul Hermann Muller, the J.R. Geigy chemist who won a Nobel Prize for reviewing, testing, and selecting DDT for the pesticide market, was previously an "investigator of dyes and tanning agents." (Encyclopedia Britannica Micropaedia (1986), v10, p322).

Generally, if not specifically, Muller had participated in the development of DDT-like chemical products which the "exhausted" FDR swallowed and/or absorbed while swimming "in the icy waters of the Bay of Fundy."

If New Jersey is said to be in the "Cancer Corridor" then would it be presumptive to call the Bay of Fundy in Roosevelt's era — "Acute Flaccid Paralysis Paradise"?

Summary Of Toxic Exposures

Many industrial toxic chemicals could have led to FDR's polio. Here is text analysis. [Table→]

| Summary of FDR Polio Causation (Environmental) | |
Mainstream Text	JW Comment
"he swam at Glensevern Pond... the water was red..."	Red may be iron oxide from pipes or tanks, indicating other chemical pollution, possibly solvents.
"he decided he wanted to swim. So he jogged two miles to swim in the icy waters of the Bay of Fundy."	Different account than below.
"fallen into the bay... sudden malaise"	This bay is downstream from toxic industries. Bay water is slow moving water where inlet effluents could accumulate. 1971 onward, bay Dolphin studies show mainly organochlorines such as PCB and CHB, with some DDT. DDT was not in use until after FDR acquired polio (1921), after 1939, but its presence indicates regional pesticide usage. Toxicity can be sudden (FDR's sudden malaise). Yet, so-called virus incubation takes a few days. Coldness and toxicity of bay may have added substantially to stress. [Cold as inflammatory trigger, not cause.]
"two mile jog through the woods to swim in a lake"	Contents of this lake water?
"a nearby island, a forest fire, which he and his son fought..."	Coup de grace: Smoke inhalation alone can paralyze, depending upon the contents of the smoke [NOx, formaldehyde, carbon monoxide, and thousands of other poison gases].

Roosevelt's acreage on Campobello is today a public park, owned jointly by the United States and Canada.

[The "Summary" table covers most toxic pollution, from pesticides to fire. It excepts stove and boiler exhaust. Since 2000, I realize those exceptions are severe neuro-stressors, emitting NOx, formaldehyde, and monoxide, etc., which create flu symptoms (misdiagnosed as virus), and these are the first symptoms of polio or other neurological diseases. Due to medical propaganda: People's usual response to "the flu" or "a cold" is bed rest and toxic pharmaceuticals for pain and fever control. Windows are closed for warmth, confining exhaust gases within the house. Fireplaces are lit for warmth, yet with windows closed, exhaust gases diffuse into the house because fireplaces need much air moving up the chimney. Boilers are turned on for heating, and tea, soup, and warm foods are cooked on unventilated gas stoves, increasing exhaust toxicity.]

Proposed Study

The strength of a theory is its ability to predict future events. Thus, in addition to the above mentioned study of DDT in dolphins, what would be the results of a comparison study regarding the statistics of neurological disease and chemical toxicity in the region of the Bay of Fundy? The pesticide/polio thesis predicts such a study would reveal a high correlation between the presence of industrial central nervous system poisons and CNS disease (such as poliomyelitis) incidence in the region of the Bay of Fundy. The pesticide/polio thesis predicts that FDR's polio would best be described by Dr. Ralph Scobey's chart on polio etiology.

[I have rendered this chart below, from Scobey's original rough (by modern standards) version, for clarification, from Scobey's article in Archives of Pediatrics (1954), "Is Polio Caused by an Exogenous Virus?" As there is no poliovirus, Scobey's chart is useful for clinical diagnostics, if we replace his word "virus" with "biomarker for poisoning".] [Graph→]

Chart 1

The Mechanism of Production of Human Poliomyelitis vs. Experimental Animal Poliomyelitis

Human Poliomyelitis

Activator	Precipitator	Biochemical Factors	
Poison/Toxin →	Fatigue Chilling Trauma Heat and Humidity Operative Procedures Pregnancy →	Genetic Agents Enzymes Hormones Mutation Physical/Chemical →	Virus

Experimental Animal Poliomyelitis

Virus → Strains → Transfer Experiment → Purification → Culture → Preventative Agents

DDT Dosage Study
Polio Epidemic of 1942-62

by Jim West (1999)

"Some foods contain enough pesticides that, if prepared for children, they can contain a nearly toxic dose." (ATSDR, U.S. Public Health Service, "Healthy Children - Toxic Environments" - 4/28/97)

"Publication of my findings drew some sharp criticism. They were characterized as 'totally without foundation,' 'highly uncontrolled,' 'hysterical' and so on. The only evidence provided in refutation was the alleged lack of toxic effect from the military and public health users of DDT... The animal work could hardly be cited because virtually all of it shows DDT to be extremely dangerous." (Morton Biskind, MD, presented before the U.S. House of Representative, 12/12/1950) [Graphs→]

Topic	Dosage mg/kg	Species	Sex	Comment	Author
Toxicity of a one dose (LD50)	113	Mouse	M	[mg/kg is equal to "ppm" in terms of weight]	Gaines (1960)
Susceptibility	25	Rat	M	largest dosage without clinical effect	Garret (1947); Hsieh (1954); Neal et al (1946); Velbinger (1947; Hayes (1959)
	6	Human		smallest dosage with clinical effect	Ibid
	16	Human		smallest dosage with serious effect (convulsions)	Ibid
	285	Human		largest nonfatal dosage (partly vomited)	Ibid
	50	Rat	M	smallest dosage with serious effect	Gaines (1960, 1969)
	175	Rat	M	largest, nonfatal dosage	Ibid
	50	Rat	M	smallest, fatal dosage	Ibid
	200	Rat	M	uniformly fatal dosage	Ibid
Susceptibility to repeated dosage	0.5 for >600 days	Human		(age not mentioned but probably adult) increased storage, no clinical effect	Hayes et al (1956)
	0.24 for 161 days	Rat	M/F	histopathological changes of the liver	Laug et al (1950)

Topic	Dosage mg/kg	Species	Sex	Comment	Author
Penetration of through the gastrointestinal tract	2% in 30 minutes	Rat		application site was the intestine, solvent was bile, method was intestinal loop [this represents the lowest GI absorption environment]	Turner and Shanks (1980)
	55% in 1 hour	Mouse		application site was oral, solvent was Emulfor, method was GI content [Emulfor is closer to the solvent efficiency of fat or milk lipids]	Ahdaya et al (1981)
Dermal penetration	34% in 1 hour	Mouse		application site was dermal, solvent was acetone, method was patch	Shah et al (1981)
	15% in 1 hour	Roach		application site was dermal, solvent was acetone, method was patch	Shah et al (1983)
	5% in 1 hour	Hornworm		application site was dermal, solvent was acetone, method was patch	Shah et al (1983)
	22% in 1 hour	Quail		application site was dermal, solvent was acetone, method was patch	Shah et al (1983)
	13% in 1 hour	Frog		application site was dermal, solvent was acetone, method was patch	Shah et al (1983)

DDT and its metabolites have also been found in numerous animal studies to be tumorigenic at very low sustained dosages, as low as 0.4 ppm. [Note: ppm is mg/kg.]

Warfarin

Warfarin [anti-coagulant at extremely small dosage] can be mixed with DDT for potentiation. [Table→]

Study (Warfarin)	mg/kg	Species	Sex	Comment	Author
Susceptibility to repeated dosage	0.14 indefinitely	Human		maintenance, therapeutic dose.	Friedman (1959)
	0.29-1.45 for 15 days	Human		hemorage in 12 people (40-70 yr) followed by recovery.	Lang and Terveer (1954)
	1.7 for 6 days	Human		hemorage in a 22 year-old man, followed by recovery.	Lange and terveer (1954)
	0.83-2.06 for 15 days	Human		Fatal to 19 year-old male and a 3 year-old girl.	Holmes and Love (1952)
	0.08 for 40 days	Rat	M/F	Fatal to 5 of 10 rats	Hayes and Gaines (1959)
	0.39 for 15 days	Rat	M/F	Fatal to 10 of 10 rats	Hayes and Gaines (1959)

13.8 ppm DDT in Milk

Just one year before polio incidence peaked, in 1951, doubts about the safety of DDT became prominent enough for U.S. government and industry to hold hearings and investigations (the Delaney Committee). These investigations allowed the number 13.8 ppm to surface regarding the highest concentration of DDT found in dairy milk. This number and other numbers found in literature are utilized in the tables below. I found 13.8ppm in Thomas R. Dunlap's book, *DDT: Scientists, Citizens, and Public Policy*, Princeton University Press (1981), p69.

In the first and second tables, 13.8ppm is used to determine how much DDT was reaching human infants and this is compared with the amount of DDT needed to cause human infant illness and death. Infants were the primary victims of polio.

The third table uses 13.8ppm to determine how much DDT was being applied to fodder crops for dairy cattle. This calculation is of more general interest and serves as an exercise to verify the previous calculations and the context of the number 13.8ppm.

Since application recommendations are never followed perfectly, due to human imperfection, error probability, and the multiple coincidence of these, it seems that ppm in milk could easily exceed the amount required in LD50 studies, thus causing illness, paralysis, and death in infants.

In the following charts, **bolded numbers** are official "givens". Regular fonts portray calculations from the given numbers.

Lethal Dosage For Infant Human
[Table→]

Human DDT concentration, for severe illness	6 mg/kg	http://grove.ucsd.edu/cruise_chem/pesteffects.html
Human DDT concentration, for death (LD50)	150 mg/kg	Dresden, *Physiological Investigations into the Action of DDT (1949)*
Infant hypersensitivity factor	12 x	See discussion below
Infant Weight	**6.4 kg**	**Assume 14 lbs, near age of highest incidence (6 to 10 months)**
Infant Illness: minimum DDT dose	4.8 mg	Calculated from above numbers. Illness could manifest as headache, nausea, fever, **porphyria**, vomiting, diarrhea, tremors, and spasms.
Infant Death: minimum DDT dose	119 mg	Calculated from above numbers. Death could arrive via fever, cough, porpdohyria, vomiting, diarrhea, spasms, nerve damage, paralysis, and suffocation due to paralysis.

Porphyria

Symptoms include photosensitivity and increased porphyrins. Porphyrins are evolutionarily ancient, nitrogen containing organic compounds that are evidence of strong anti-oxidizing activity within the body.

From Hayes and Laws, p90-91:

> "Coproporphyrin III... Found in normal urine, increased in urine of persons with **poliomyelitis**, those treated with salvarsan [arsenic compound], and those **poisoned** by lead and hexachlorobenzene; increased in urine in most cases of acute porphyria but rarely in congenital porphyria; greatly increased in feces in hexachlorobenzene-induced porphyria."

> "Protoporphyrin III... Found in urine in pellagra and feces in hexachlorobenzene-induced porphyria."

> "Some increase in the concentration of porphyrins in the blood and urine accompanies lead poisoning in humans so frequently that one is forced to conclude that lead causes a direct injury to some aspect of porphyrin metabolism and does not merely trigger the effect in the genetically susceptible. The same is true of abnormal porphyrin metabolism in persons with infectious **hepatitis, poliomyelitis, pellagra, and pernicious anemia**."

Dr. Ralph Scobey wrote:

> "There are two abnormal findings in cases of **poliomyelitis** that point strongly to poisoning as the cause of this disease. One consists in the appearance of increased amounts of **porphyrin** in the urine; the other is the presence of increased amounts of guanidine in the blood. It is a well-known fact that porphyria can follow

poisoning by a number of chemicals. Guanidine has
been found in increased amounts in the blood in arsenic,
chloroform, and carbon tetrachloride poisonings."

Scobey also phrased the information slightly differently,
elsewhere:

"A study of the biochemical changes that arise during
the course of human poliomyelitis has not been followed
adequately, but a few important clues have been
reported. One of these consists of the presence of
coproporphyrin III in the urine of poliomyelitis
patients[96]; another is the appearance in the blood of
increased amounts of guanidine. It is not to be
overlooked that both of these chemicals are present in
the body in increased amounts in cases of poisoning by a
number of toxic agents."

It has been attempted for decades to define pellagra as a
virus-caused disease. Eventually, it began to be known to be
the result of nutritional deficiencies. However, its alignment
with porphyria herein may rejuvenate the discussion, as
pellagra also may be actually the result of pesticides -- with
the nutritional argument being a compromise with industry.

Infant Hypersusceptibility

This is a powerful factor, often neglected in presentations of
DDT toxicity. Infants generally have much greater
susceptibility to neurotoxins because their nervous system is
in a state of rapid growth up until about the 7th year. At birth,
much of an infant's nerve system is not protected with a
myelin sheath and the sheathing process continues up to the
7th year.

Because of the (understandable) lack of available studies
regarding human infant hypersusceptibility to DDT, this
factor has been estimated, as follows: In animal studies it is

known that DDT can be passed via milk through two nursing female hosts to kill the infant offspring of the second host. Because the excretion of DDT is 1/4 of the ingested DDT in a nursing female, the infant factor for hypersusceptibility is at least 16.

In other words, at least 1/16th (i.e., 1/4 x 1/4) of the DDT ingested by the first nursing female does reach the infant offspring of the second female host and this relatively small amount is enough to kill the infants via nerve damage and paralysis, while leaving the adult female hosts apparently unharmed, giving us a minimum hypersusceptibility factor of 16.

The fraction 1/4 is from *Modern Toxicology* (1997), p114, and refers to experiments with dairy cows. The study of two female hosts is from Daniel Dresden's *Physiological Investigations into the Action of DDT* (1949) and refers to the first host as a nursing female goat and the second host as a nursing female rat.

A likely criticism of this approach could be that in this consideration there is a variety of carrier media (food types): the dairy cow eats mostly grass and beans, the female rat drinks goat milk, and the rat's infant offspring drink rat milk. Thus there is a variability of DDT absorption into the host. A defense is that the variability is negligible because dairy fodder, whole grass and beans, contains fats and proteins, as does milk, and that these are efficient carriers of DDT, and that dairy cows have a powerful digestive system, they thoroughly digest through mastication, regurgitation and re-mastication, giving ample opportunity for DDT to be integrated into the fatty component of the nutrients, building a DDT carrier approximating the efficiency of milk. It is likely that 1/4 would apply also to the female goat since its diet and digestive system are similar enough to the dairy cow. To give critics the benefit, larger fractions than 1/4, such as 1/3 to 1/2 are applied herein to the female rat (which drinks the goat's milk), assuming that milk is a more efficient DDT carrier than grass. Therefore, the range of susceptibility would range from 8 to 12 (inversions of 1/4 x 1/2 to 1/4 x 1/3). Since 8 and 12 are minimums, we should assume them to be closer to 12 to 18 and the average of these is 15.

General studies of chemical susceptibility in infants vs adults has arrived at hypersusceptibility numbers as high as 750 for some chemicals. Hayes and Laws uncritically report as factual, that infant rats are less sensitive to DDT than infants. However, the "two adult hosts" phenomena above, and numerous statements throughout toxicology literature clearly contradict Hayes and Laws' defense of DDT. The considerations above arrive reasonably at a minimum infant hypersusceptibility factor of 12, which is used herein.

Pesticides News (Issue No. 40, June 1998) states:

> "In 1994, one fatal poisoning was reported in the US involving a child who ingested one ounce (28g) of a 5% DDT and kerosene solution."
> http://www.gn.apc.org/pesticidestrust/aifacts/ddt.htm [Defunct URL, alternate: www.pan-uk.org/pestnews/Actives/ddt.htm rev 2014])

The above fatal dosage works out to 1.4g of DDT, i.e., 77 mg/kg for the child (estimated at 40 lbs, due to no weight provided in reference). [Rev 2014.] In this incident the level of child susceptibility translates to about five times higher than for an adult. Since the LD50 is the number where 50% of a group dies at a given dosage, with some dying at much lower dosages and some at much higher dosages, 77 mg/kg may represent only the middle range of lethal susceptibility. Therefore, susceptibility could be much greater.

Infant Dosage Of DDT In 1953

DDT In milk (official high number)	13.8	ppm	Dunlap (op. cit.)
Milk ingested by infant per day	700	grams	Handbook of Pesticide Toxicity, p306
DDT ingested by 14 lb infant per day	9.7	mg	Calculated

9.6 mg DDT per infant per day falls into the range of the first table for infant illness. Thus the potential for illness due to DDT dosage clearly existed in the U.S. in the 1950s, using 13.8ppm. Since this does not account for accumulative dosage, and DDT does accumulate in the body, with it and its metabolites having a half-life of almost one year, a real danger exists for polio-like diseases due to pesticide exposure in milk. This data, in addition to the direct correlation of DDT production with polio incidence, and the similarity of the physiologies of DDT toxicity and polio give ample reason to suspect DDT causality for poliomyelitis, other CNS diseases.

My "normal" experience as a child growing up in the 1950s included frequent colds and flu, headache, fever, photosensitivity, nausea, diarrhea, stiff neck, measles, mumps, boils, and pink eye -- the clinical descriptions of non-paralytic polio.

Cross-Check

The following tables show the relationships between DDT application, DDT residue on grass, cow ingestion of DDT and how these numbers show a coherent relation to 13.8 ppm. This gives a wider perspective and acts as a partial cross check for the tables above. Authorities must have been aware of this numerical context as they arrived at the number 13.8 ppm.

DDT, Pasture Grass, and Milk Per Cow

		Source
DDT retained on pasture grass	10 percent	Van Nostrand Enc. of Science and Technology (1995), p1725
DDT ingested by cow and excreted in cow's milk	25 percent	Modern Toxicology (1997), p114
Milk per cow per year	2,769 kg	Encyclopedia Britannica (1906)
Pasture required for one cow	3.5 acres	Encyclopedia Britannica (1906)

DDT ppm, Recommended Usage

The above numbers are used to generate the following table:
[Table→]

DDT in milk (official high number)	13.8	ppm	Dunlap (op. cit.)
DDT excreted in milk per cow per year	0.038	kg	
DDT retained on pasture grass, eaten by cow	.15	kg	
DDT applied to pasture grass per cow	1.53	kg	
DDT applied to pasture grass per acre	.44	kg	i.e., 1 pound/acre, the generally recommended application for DDT, Toxic Terror: The Truth Behind The Cancer Scares (1992)

The official given numbers in the above two tables are pat, i.e., they fit together too well. Were officials pondering such a table before they came up with 13.8ppm? It is interesting to see that the recommended application amount of 1 lb per acre works out to 13.8ppm of DDT in cow's milk. If there is a relation between the recommended application concentration and DDT ppm then it appears that a high average ppm for recent years" was reported as "the highest ppm". If we accept these figures what would be the probability that they could be exceeded due to combinations of error, ignorance, aggressive purpose in application, or deliberate sabotage?

Biskind writes that the Dept. of Agriculture study found a range of DDT in dairy milk of from 0.5ppm to 25ppm. (M. Biskind, MD, "Clinical Intoxication From DDT", *Journal of Insurance Medicine*, May 1951, p9)

DDT In Human Milk

Hayes and Laws state that the first studies regarding DDT in human milk were by Laug in 1951, even though Biskind reported human milk studies in April, 1949 where a concentration of 116ppm is found in the milk of a woman who had been under study for neuropsychiatric disorders, whereby, suspecting a toxic cause, her milk was analyzed for DDT levels immediately after she gave birth. The results were: 116ppm, 18ppm, 2ppm, 5ppm, 5ppm. Apparently such extreme numbers are only found when tests include the colostrum (milk excreted just after birth). Milk excretion is known to be a form of toxin catharsis for adult females, at the expense of their offspring.

The Laug study on human milk came out a year after Biskind's report, so perhaps Laug's study, based in Washington, D.C., was in response to Biskind's progress. Laug utilized Negro women (only) for his studies of DDT in human fat tissue and human milk. The milk studies utilized

"32 samples from 32 different Negro women outpatients from a District of Columbia Hospital...". It is interesting to note that during the first major worldwide polio epidemic in 1916, Negros were considered immune to polio. It is possible that this "immunity" was conferred for dietary reasons, as it is commonly known that the high consumption of dairy products is primarily a European habit, often not shared by those of African descent.

Hayes and Laws report 0.13ppm as the concentration given for DDT in human milk according to studies by Laug et al (1951). Hayes and Laws do not mention that this is an average. If we look at the original Laug publication we find that 0.13ppm is a mean average and that the high was 0.77ppm.

If the first human milk at birth (mentioned by Biskind and not measured by Laug) can contain as high as 116ppm DDT, then the DDT in commercial dairy milk must have reached much higher ppm since animal standards are much lower regarding pesticide exposure. Cows may have eaten fodder that was treated with pesticides. Cows were often treated with 5% DDT solutions during feeding (Zimmerman, O.T., Ph.D., Lavine, Irvin, Ph.D., *DDT - Killer of Killers*, Industrial Research Service, Dover, New Hampshire (1946)).

DDT can also be absorbed through the skin of dairy animals and concentrate in their milk.

Officially, DDT levels were 106 times higher in dairy milk compared to human milk (13.8ppm vs .13ppm) [apparently of those] who preferred a diet low in dairy products or the officials were trying to spin down human DDT ppm. Infants fed exclusively on human milk do not get polio, according to an investigation into the diet of polio victims by a Massachusetts State Health Inspector, during an epidemic in 1908. Albert Sabin wrote in May, 1950 that human milk and "certain" cow's milk conferred protection from polio. In 1949, it was reported that Eskimo polio epidemics did not affect breastfed Eskimo infants.

The NYC epidemic of 1916 rarely affected infants under the age of 6 months. This information is reflected in the following graph of Haven Emerson's data on age and polio incidence: [Graph→]

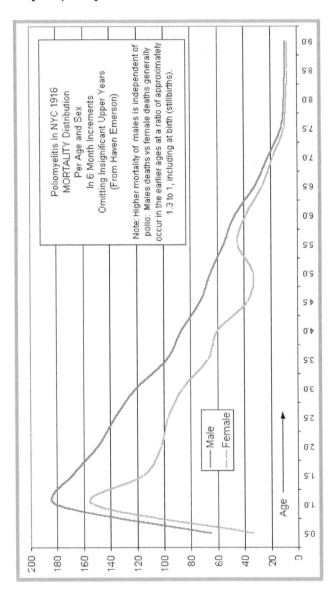

Poliomyelitis In NYC 1916
MORTALITY Distribution
Per Age and Sex
In 6 Month Increments
Omitting Insignificant Upper Years
(From Haven Emerson)

Note: Higher mortality of males is independent of polio. Males deaths vs female deaths generally occur in the earlier ages at a ratio of approximately 1.3 to 1, including at birth (stillbirths).

In the 1950s, when DDT became ubiquitous at high dosages, the age curve flattened out to include older children.

Scobey reported that, "In 1908, [during] an epidemic of poliomyelitis... no infant who was fed exclusively on the breast developed poliomyelitis."

It is interesting to tentatively view the vertical axis as "Dairy Milk As Percent Of Diet", as in 1916, such a graph would likely have the same shape.

In 1946, when the Great Polio Epidemic was exploding, Zimmerman and Lavine advocated that farmers spray 5% DDT solutions upon dairy animals during feeding, in the air, upon their bodies and bedding.

Political Efficiency

In the early 1950s, when the average dietary level for the U.S. population in the early 1950s was reported to be 5ppm, rat studies showed that liver damage was being caused at dietary levels of DDT at 5ppm (generally, high dosages of pesticides are recognized soon because of nerve damage, and repeated low dosages over a longer period of time cause cell and membrane damage, first apparent in the liver.)

Biskind (1953) wrote:

> "In 1950, a year in which more than 200 million pounds of insecticides were used in agriculture alone in this country, investigators of the Federal Food and Drug Administration announced: The finding of hepatic [liver] cell alteration at dietary levels as low as 5ppm of DDT, and the considerable storage of the chemical at levels that might well occur in some human diets, makes

it extremely likely that the potential hazard of DDT has been underestimated."

In 1951, the United States Public Health Service pointed out:

"DDT is a delayed-action poison. Due to the fact that it accumulates in the body tissues, especially in females, the repeated inhalation or ingestion of DDT constitutes a distinct health hazard. The deleterious effects are manifested principally in the liver, spleen, kidneys and spinal cord."

"DDT is excreted in the milk of cows and of nursing mothers after exposure to DDT sprays and after consuming food contaminated with this poison. Children and infants especially are much more susceptible to poisoning than adults."

In spite of Biskind's warnings and the evidence, by 1956 the National Research Council stated in "Safe Uses of Pesticides In Food Production", regarding pesticide law before 1954, that:

"...the old procedures had protected the public, as shown by the absence of authenticated association of pesticide residues with human illness..."

A mouse study in 1973 found DDT to be tumorigenic at dosages of .25 mg/kg (Terracini et al). Another mouse study found DDT tumorigenic at 2 mg/kg (Tomatis et al). In 1969 a mouse study found a DDT metabolite to be tumorigenic at the range of 0.4 to 0.7 mg/kg (Innes et al). Yet, DDT's relation to cancer is still said to be questionable.

Summary

Biskind wrote that he was attacked via the citing of false data, such as, the purported safety of DDT among army personnel, although Albert B. Sabin had found that U.S. army personnel in the Philippines (treated heavily with DDT) suffered more than 10 times the poliomyelitis as the army personnel in the U.S. Additionally, Sabin wrote that polio was the leading cause of death next to battle casualties and that soldiers in DDT-treated areas suffered a great variety of severe illnesses, as opposed to soldiers in untreated areas who were "without ailments of any sort" according to interviews of soldiers by Biskind.

The points made herein can be summarized in two graphs. Various dosages and hypersusceptibility factors are presented below. Assumed is a 14 lb infant, drinking 700 grams of milk per day, and the resulting vertical axis is "Days To Accumulate Illness Dosage" in the first table and "Days To Accumulate Death Dosage" in the second. These graphs demonstrate that between the two extremes (illness and death) exists an impressive array of possibilities for DDT causality.

Infant Illness

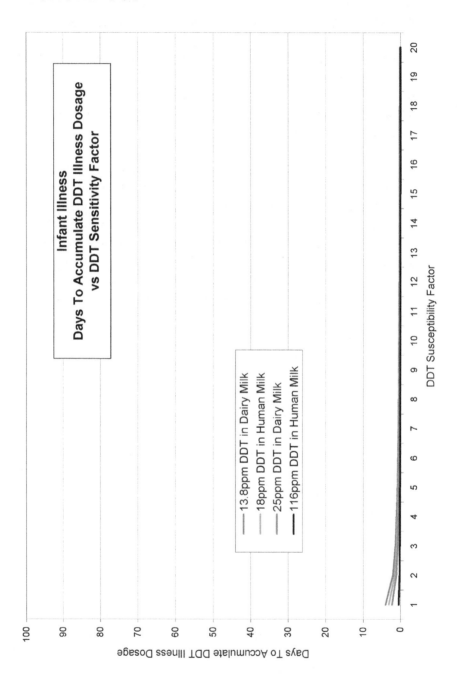

Infant Death

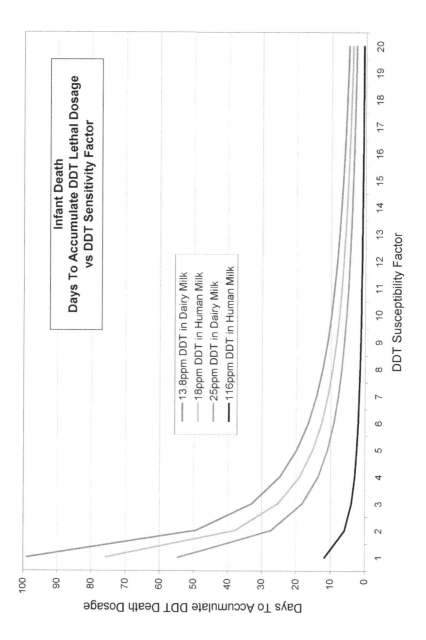

Criticism of this approach could be that:

1) "Days To Accumulate DDT Dosage" does not consider that DDT is converted to metabolites of more or less toxicity after ingestion.

2) DDT is stored after ingestion in "safer" areas of the body such as in fatty tissue.

The rebut of such criticism is that:

1) DDT does not readily metabolize to significantly less toxic or non-toxic forms.

2) Repeated dosages at the levels found in human diets over a 2 to 60 day period are known to cause neurological disease.

3) Once any susceptibility factors are included, the criticism exponentially becomes invalid.

4) At dosages of 25ppm or 116ppm, criticism clearly becomes invalid.

5) During periods of fasting, fat storage is metabolized and pesticides can be released at potentially dangerous levels.

6) Fatty tissue includes the myelin, which is the nerve sheath. Thus DDT accumulates in the nerve sheath and has obvious opportunities to cause nerve damage.

The Positive Results of DDT/Polio Research

by Jim West, 2014

Data Availability

Prior to 2000, I could find no mention of the two words, "polio" and "pesticides", on the same internet page. Neither could the two words be found in any single article in *The New York Times*, or any single article anywhere. There was no mention of the polio arcana, i.e., works by the Biskind, Mobbs, Scobey, in terms of polio and pesticides. The arcana virtually did not exist in footnotes, except as a warning in Hayes & Laws, to avoid them. Similarly, they were not found in NIH *PubMed* online library.

June 2000, my article was published in *Townsend Letter*, with the arcana pushed to the foreground for authority.

Nowadays, the two words are commonly found together on the internet and sometimes spoken on radio; there is a growing awareness. Sometimes the two words are found together even in mainstream forums, though, as a target with dissident rebuttal disallowed.

Circa 2006, I encountered as usual, the old norm in the mainstream. I referenced the arcana on *Wikipedia's* polio topic "Talk" page, because the main page is heavily guarded. The entire Talk Page was soon deleted, "archived" away.

Poliovirus Not Isolated

Less than a year later, an article appeared April 2001, on the website of the biochemist, Howard Urnovitz, PhD. The article was written by Neenyah Ostrom and authorized by Urnovitz.

The article applies Perthian Deconstruction (my term) of HIV to poliovirus. The Perth Group had, in the 1980s, make it very clear that HIV virus isolation has not been demonstrated, thus invalidating studies that claim to have characterized HIV. The Perth Group consists of university academics, not virologists, and so they were more able to truthfully critique virology, less hampered by the politics of the profession of virology. The mainstream avoids them as much as possible, and prevents them from contributing to their own Wikipedia page.

The article finds that the famous laboratory studies of poliovirus, which claim virus isolation, had not actually isolated a virus. The article carefully examines the work of the revered virologists Enders, Dulbecco, Vogt, Dalldorf, Sickles, Salk, etc. A common practice of virology is criticized whereby virologists claim virus isolation by extracting a clear supernatant (top layer) from a blended and centrifuged puree of feces.

> "Dalldorf and Sickles used the word 'isolation' to describe their creation of a suspension of fecal matter which was a vast overstatement, to put it mildly."

Scientists claim isolation of viruses by obtaining an adverse reaction from an infant mouse, by drilling a hole through its skull and injecting the supernatant into its brain. They use extremely vulnerable injection targets such as genetically bred immune-deficient mice, egg embryos on the most vulnerable day of maturation, and diseased cells, e.g., laboratory cancer cell lines and immune deficient leukemia cell lines that are grown perpetually in laboratories in a solution of poisons (antibiotics).

The article make it clear that poliovirus isolation has not been achieved. The article is no longer presented on the Urnovitz site, and an online search finds that his foray into virological criticism appears short-lived. He may have met mainstream repression. He was confronted strongly by the dissident side also, as The Perth Group successfully challenged him with regard to HIV topics, where Urnovitz may have attempted to hold onto theories dear to his profession. That debate occurred on Nicholas Regush's now defunct website, *Red Flag Daily*, circa 2002.

As a public service, I preserved the article on my websites, harvoa.org and harpub.tk. Urnovitz deserves huge credit for putting his professional neck on the line, making a major professional historical statement. In 2001, I was fortunate to have met the friendly and helpful Dr. Urnovitz at the office of Nicholas Regush, journalist and producer at ABC News headquarters in Manhattan (my work on West Nile epidemics had the interest of Regush, who wrote a major article, published by ABC, in August 2001, based on our conversations. Regush is deceased, as of 2004).

Quotes from the Ostrom-Urnovitz article:

> "Early poliomyelitis researchers [from 1908, throughout the early 20th century...] Flexner, Lewis, Dalldorf, Landsteiner, Popper, Dulbecco, Sabin, Salk, and many others worked with unknown agents. They didn't understand the properties of the contaminated tissues they handled... early 20th century researchers should not get a free pass for their lack of precision in describing experiments and their results."

> Dalldorf and Sickles [1948] used the word "isolation" to describe their creation of a suspension of fecal matter which was a vast overstatement, to put it mildly.

"...Dulbecco and Vogt... simply pipetted some liquid ('plaque stock') from one culture plate and replated it onto other culture plates. [...they] went further than they had evidence to support. They asserted not only that they had isolated poliovirus, but that, 'these stocks constitute the purest lines of virus presently available.' [...They] did not isolate pure poliovirus in any of the experiments described in [their] 1954 report. While they write of seeding their cultures with 'virus', they actually used unpurified suspensions, not pure viral isolates. ...a perfectly tautological proof [via cyclic logic]."

"[WHO and CDC guidelines, both published in 2000, were reviewed for poliovirus detection. Regarding CDC's] time-honored method of detecting the poliovirus and the body's response to it, it does not 'isolate' the poliovirus, it simply detects poliovirus [see note]. The samples tested by the CDC and WHO should be described as 'poliovirus reactive material,' not as samples that contain isolated, pure poliovirus. Once again, we have no proof that poliovirus has been isolated."

Note the phrase, "detects poliovirus", which should be, in the spirit of the article, "detects supposed poliovirus". Otherwise, this phrase might be an attempt to diminish political complications. In latter paragraphs, the article calls the early polio scientists "pioneers" and praises their "bravery" apparently as an attempt to maintain a safe political balance.

Perhaps the phrase is meant to be as is, in anticipation of the possibility that there actually may be a hidden or overlooked study that achieved poliovirus isolation, and that the test methods were constructed upon such actual isolates. That possibility can be strongly refuted.

The article had already demonstrated the great claims of poliovirus isolation to be false. We can be sure, with certainty, there cannot be any real isolates because the real achievement of poliovirus isolation would have been bannered around the world's headlines with the greatest fanfare superceding any fame garnered by Enders, Dulbecco, Vogt, Landsteiner, Popper, etc. Even if a poliovirus isolate were found (extremely unlikely), the character of any supposed virus isolate cannot be known if the toxicology of the disease, or of any bioeffect related to the virus, is not discounted, and toxicology is virtually never discounted.

In terms of research, poliovirus is the most funded virus ever, with the possible exception of HIV. Criticism of poliovirus propaganda thus has great impact on the many other less-studied so-called viruses.

Strange DDT Advocates

After 2000, there has been a revival of DDT advocacy, well publicized, defending DDT from on high. It attacks images of Rachel Carson, even bringing about accusations of genocide. Carson's popular devaluation of DDT is claimed to have brought an end to the malaria mosquito programs. The attacks are superficial and ill-founded, yet enough to convert even some environmentalists to the pro-DDT stance.

It is unlikely that malaria is a valid disease paradigm because the paradigm was not constructed properly, i.e., it omitted environmental toxicology. Toxicity is obviously a potential cause for malaria, because the great epidemics followed the widespread introduction of arsenic-lead pesticides in 1868 in industrial non-tropical countries, and continued on until the introduction of organochlorine pesticides and fumigants near the beginning of the 20th century. Nowadays malaria is considered a disease of the tropics.

In 1895, Captain Ross discovered the malaria parasite cycle. 40 years later, he introduced his autobiography, honest enough to wonder with distaste why no one had challenged or confirmed his work. Implicit in his wondering is that polluting industrial power has an interest and maintains his work. Ross's notebooks reveal that human macrophages easily digest the malaria parasite if the blood is at normal temperature, yet the cold-blooded mosquito has no defense against the parasite which easily destroys its internal organs. While in Africa, during his work of discovery, he received letters from his professional medical contact in England, indicating great rewards if he focused on the parasite paradigm.

Diagnostics are contradictory. The various malaria parasite species and the symptoms of malaria do not consistently associate causatively. Either often exists without the other and toxicology is avoided.

I postulate an interpretation of Ross, that the parasite may be a symbiont that behaves unnaturally when the human internal microbial ecology is put out of balance by pollution. A parallel: Chemist and dentist Gerard Judd writes that the protective microbial flora living in dental gums will cause odors and gum disease due to fluoride disturbing the micro-ecological balance within the gum flora. Another parallel: Normal, omnipresent streptococci bacteria, protective bacteria, suddenly appear as "deadly" alternate forms due to toxic exposure. The mainstream demonizes such streptococci while avoiding the relevant toxicology.

The malaria campaigns have been admitted by some officials to be a failure, campaigns that are just to be doing something. Carson could be a convenient excuse for cancelling those campaigns, and placing them into a perpetual veiled state of politically enhancing argument.

Michel Crichton (deceased) promoted DDT as harmless. He is promoted as the famous intellect and author, a plot source for Spielberg films. In a C-SPAN video his tenuous position becomes obvious as he responds to a high school student who questions his pro-DDT stance. Angrily, Crichton plays several emotional cards by invoking "Hitler" and "Stalin" to describe a malaria holocaust as the result of Euro-American industrial countries denying "people of color" the benefits of DDT anti-mosquito programs, simply because "we don't care... we don't have malaria...".

A well-publicized DDT proponent is Steven Milloy, a slinger of the phrase, "Junk Science". Milloy has worked on behalf of chemical companies, defending their dubious products in major media, as described by Tim Lambert, where Milloy is called an "industry shill". *Sourcewatch* has a run-down on Milloy, describing his monetary ties with tobacco and petrochemical corporations. Though registered as a Monsanto lobbyist, Milloy denies that he lobbies. Wikipedia writes, "Milloy has criticized a number of other corporations for adopting environmental initiatives..." Milloy is published by *The New York Times*, and others, without apology, as Milloy trashes Carson and promotes DDT while proclaiming "genocide" due to the discontinuation of DDT to kill mosquitoes in malaria epidemic regions.

DDT-Eaters

Professor J. Gordon Edwards coauthored pro-DDT material with Milloy. According an interview article of Edwards, he routinely ate DDT powder in order to convince his audience that DDT was harmless. He also cried that DDT critics are responsible for "genocide", via malaria.

Edwards was misleading his audience with a stunt, as I assume he must have known. Edwards would only be saved from disaster by the fact that DDT does not readily dissolve in water. Eating or drinking DDT with only water, saliva, watery GI tract juices, minimizes DDT hazards. DDT is a waxy substance and is carried in fat, oil, and soap emulsions. DDT is a destructive neurotoxin when its chlorine atoms are carried to the nervous system via fats or fatty emulsions, not water. Examples are meat fats and dairy products. The EPA has reviewed many DDT studies and these studies do clearly show DDT to be a grave hazard.

Dr. Rutledge Taylor and Dr. Elizabeth Whelan promote a dramatic documentary of the genocide theme, *3 Billion and Counting.* The film defends DDT and demonizes Rachel Carson's views. Rutledge drinks DDT powder with water to demonstrate DDT as harmless. Videos of Rutledge claiming DDT is harmless and drinking DDT are online at YouTube. The pro-DDT documentary film states that EPA, Sierra Club, Greenpeace, and the World Wildlife Fund "refused interviews. Does that reveal conflict of interest among the well-funded environmental groups? They could have easily made fools of the DDT-Eaters and sharply contradicted the film's thesis.

DDT and Water

With water, the waxy DDT powder passes through the human GI tract mostly unabsorbed. However, if Edwards were to drink DDT powder emulsified into warm milk (a fat-aqueous emulsion), he would not have fared well. Such hazards exist on vegetables or fruits sprayed with DDT emulsions. In that more realistic scenario, Edwards would have emulated the fate of infants that ingested DDT in dairy milk during the 1950s.

A 1951, USDA studies determined DDT to be the cause of paralysis of calves, a parallel of human infantile paralysis, polio.

Daniel Dresden's studies, mentioned in my *Townsend Letter* article,describes milk/DDT emulsion animal experiments. One of his studies in particular shows the powerful toxicity of DDT when emulsified in milk. A female animal was fed DDT emulsified in milk. A second female was then fed breastmilk of the first female. The second female then suckled her infant, which became paralyzed, and thereby the nervous system of the suckling infant is proven to be extremely vulnerable.

According to Biskind, before the Great Polio Epidemic of 1945-1972, the FDA predicted a neurological epidemic from DDT. The FDA had done the studies and attempted to prevent the DDT invasion. During the upswing of polio incidence, government inspectors mandated DDT on dairy farms. His articles could not be published as of the early 1950s. I found that with the decline of polio, the government mandate ruled the opposite, i.e., against DDT on dairy farms. DDT was advertised as harmless during the upswing of polio, and with the decline, DDT required warning labels.

DDT can bring paralysis to both humans and insects. Yet Edwards said, "no human beings have ever been harmed by DDT." Official statements also make such absolute claims. Yet, they, of course, misrepresent. Statistical analysis of distribution curves, of DDT-application statistics that include the probability of human error on a global scale, would reveal the likely harm that is occurring from DDT.

See my DDT Dosage Study, where a mere 16 mg/kg DDT dosage results in severe clinical effect during rat lab studies. A mere 6 mg/kg results in a threshold clinical effect, and a miniscule 0.24 mg/kg applied repeatedly for 161 days results in liver bioeffects.

Author

Jim West grew up in Arizona where he had the good fortune to experience beautiful natural deserts, mountains, and sky scapes. During his youth he witnessed the expansion of Phoenix into a major polluted metropolis, with the clear blue mountains that surrounded the Valley of the Sun, now hidden behind industrial smog.

He has devoted much of his life to the study of medical science and politics, a study initiated at an very early age as a matter of survival. He has a scientific background, with a university level education in engineering, physics, chemistry, advanced math and various psychologies, though without completing his degree. He is self-taught in microbiology, biochemistry, toxicology, electronics and computer assembly language. He has some commercial achievement in designing chemical products. He has served as the Chairman of the Science Committee for the No Spray Coalition and is a member of GreenSpeakers, a Toastmasters group.

He has no official professional or authoritative capacity.

He is a dedicated researcher, journalist and advocate for the environment and responsible industry. He sees significant research advantages beyond those in official professional capacities. With less political complications, uncluttered thought is possible. The non-official is able to critique the professional medical mainstream in areas of scientific truth where a professional can be limited by a web of beliefs, rules and laws influenced by vested interests.

Find more at http://harvoa.org

Copyright

Made in United States
North Haven, CT
17 February 2024

48854286R00052